This **GO DIEGO GO!** Annual

belongs to:

....

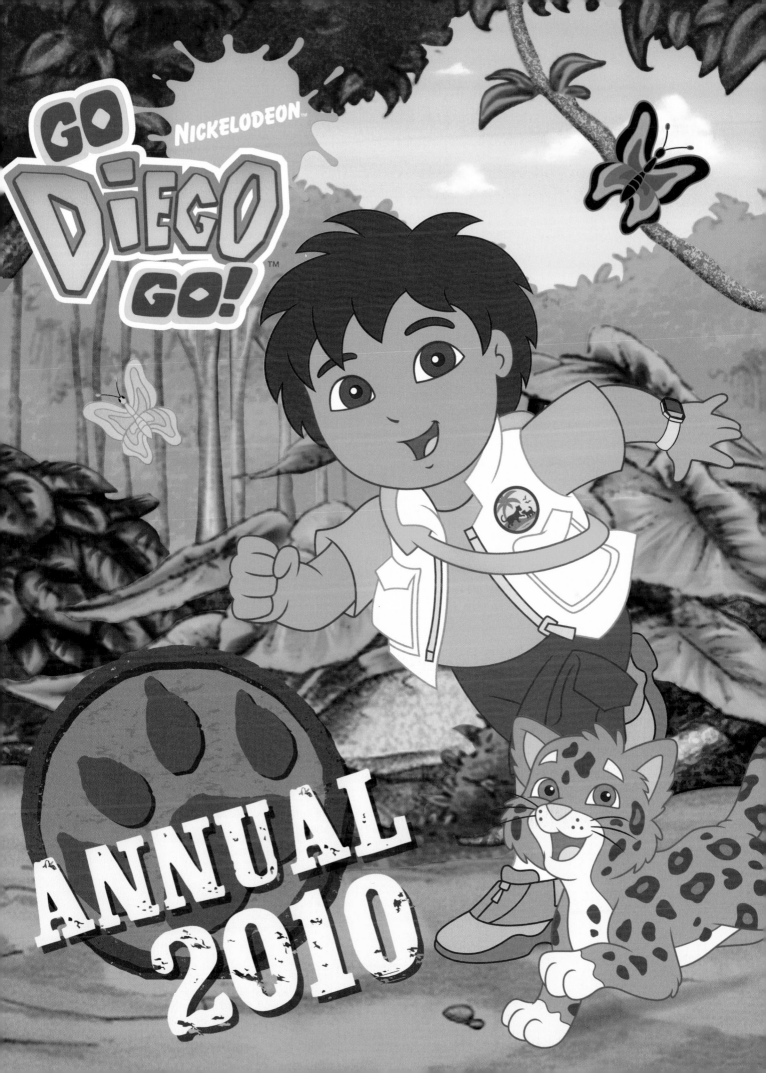

Contents

EGMONT

We bring stories to life

First published in Great Britain 2009 by Egmont UK Limited
239 Kensington High Street, London W8 6SA
Created for Egmont by John Brown
Editorial: Chloe Martin, Claire Baker • Design: Geordie Toogood

© 2009 Viacom International Inc.
All rights reserved.
Nickelodeon, Nick Jr., Go, Diego, Go! and all related titles, logos
and characters are trademarks of Viacom International Inc.

ISBN 978 1 4052 4641 5
1 3 5 7 9 10 8 6 4 2
Printed in Italy

Join in every day on Nick Jr.
www.nickjr.co.uk

Diego Saves Baby River Dolphin

It's the rainy season and there are puddles everywhere. The river has flooded the rainforest! Some of the animals might need our help. Come on, let's go!

Squeak!

Squeak!

Can you hear a squeaking noise? That sounds like an animal in trouble. My special camera, Click, can help us find out what animal it is.

Click says it's a baby river dolphin. He's stuck in the rainforest and he can't get back to the river where his mami is. We've got to save him!

SPANISH
to the rescue, my friends
al rescate, amigos
say 'al res-KAH-tay, ah-MEE-gohs'

Did you know river dolphins change colour from grey to pink as they grow older? We need to get Baby River Dolphin back to his mami before he changes colour. ¡Al rescate, amigos!

We found Baby River Dolphin! Now let's take him back to his mami. We need to get up the river, but there are leaves blocking our way. Look, Baby River Dolphin has used his beak 'nose' to clear the leaves! Let's follow him.

START

Oh no! Baby River Dolphin hasn't noticed he's heading towards a waterfall! We need to warn him. Say "Watch out. ¡Cuidado!" He needs to get away from the waterfall quickly.

SPANISH
watch out
cuidado
say 'kwee-DAH-doh'

River dolphins can flap their tails to swim backwards. Say "Swim backwards, Baby River Dolphin!" Flap your arms like a tail to help him. Great, he's safe!

Oh dear – those naughty Bobo Brothers have thrown broken branches into the river. Tick (✓) the photograph that Click took as they did it.

River dolphins can twist their bodies to get through tight spaces. If Baby River Dolphin twists, he will be able to get around the branches. Twist your body from side to side to help him. You did it. Well done!

Answer on page 68.

Well done – we helped Baby River Dolphin get back to his mami! Tick (✓) the right box to show whether each river dolphin fact is true or false.

River dolphins turn orange as they get older.

true ◯   false ✓

River dolphins can swim backwards.

true ✓   false ◯

River dolphins use their noses to move leaves.

true ◯   false ✓

Answers on page 68.

Animal Match

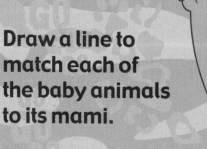

Draw a line to match each of the baby animals to its mami.

SPANISH
mummy
mami
say 'MAH-mee'

Draw a circle around the animal whose mami isn't here.

**There are eight bugs hiding in the rainforest!
Count them and write the number 8 in the box.**

**Put the dolphins in size order. Write the letters a, b, c and d in
the correct order in the boxes, starting with a as the largest.**

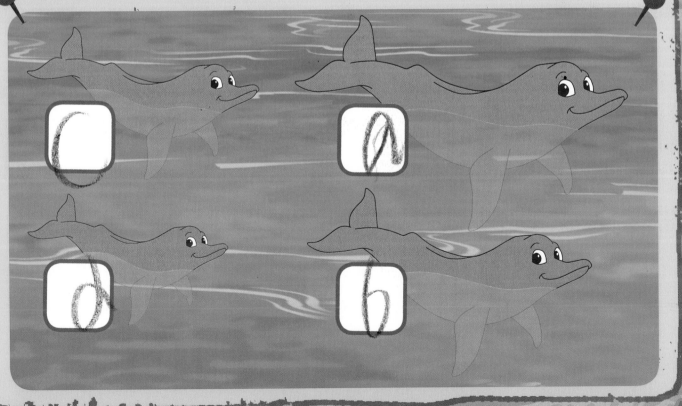

Diego's Animal Facts

Diego knows all about animals – do you?
Match each animal to a fact by writing
the animal's number in the right box.

1 Jaguar

2 Crocodile

3 Elephant

4 Spider

18

This strong swimmer has a long scaly tail!

This animal's spots help it to hide in the rainforest.

This animal has eight long legs!

This big animal has a trunk.

I'm an animal expert. ¡Soy experto de animales!

Answers on page 68.

Gorilla Fun!

Look at the pictures, then read Diego's story and say the words out loud.

Juma · Baby gorilla · Click · Drum · Hole · Video watch · Buffalo

¡Hola! My friend [Juma] has invited us to a party to crown the new [baby gorilla] king.

The [drum] beats to start the party, but the [baby gorilla] is nowhere to be seen! [Click] soon finds the [baby gorilla]. He is stuck in a [hole] in the jungle. Let's rescue him! At the [hole], we find not one [baby gorilla] but two!

Let's help to pull them out – pull! Great.

20

Now we need to send  a message on the  to tell him the news. On the way back, each  tries to frighten away some  by beating his chest like a . It works! Now they can join the party and be crowned Kings of the Mountain!

Can you beat your chest like a drum? ¡Excelente!

SPANISH

excellent
excelente
say 'ex-seh-LEN-tay'

Gorilla Puzzles

22

Write in the first letter of each animal. The letters spell out something that the baby gorillas wore at the party. What is it?

C rocodile

r abbit

o tter

W oodpecker

n ewt

The baby gorillas wore a

___ ___ ___ ___ ___

Draw lines to join up the three pairs of matching gorillas!

Answers on page 68.

Journey to Jaguar Mountain

¡Hola! Today Baby Jaguar wants to climb Jaguar Mountain for the very first time. Jaguars are great climbers because they have really sharp claws.

SPANISH
come with me
ven conmigo
say 'ven
con-ME-goh'

I need to find Mama Jaguar and take her to the Mountain. Then Baby Jaguar can surprise her when he climbs to the top. Come with me. ¡Ven conmigo! See you later, Baby Jaguar – we'll meet you there!

Come on, Mama Jaguar, let's go! Uh–oh, this wind is really strong. It's blown that tree over and trapped Rescue Pack. Let's help Mama Jaguar push the tree and free him. Push with your hands. Keep pushing!

SPANISH
thanks
gracias
say 'GRAH-see-ass'

¡Gracias! You helped free Rescue Pack. But now we need to find Mama Jaguar again. She's hard to see in the rainforest because her orange fur and dark spots blend in with the colours around her.

Click has taken photos all around the rainforest, but the photo captions have got muddled up!

Read the captions, then write in the number of the matching photo in each box.

Two butterflies flutter past some flowers.

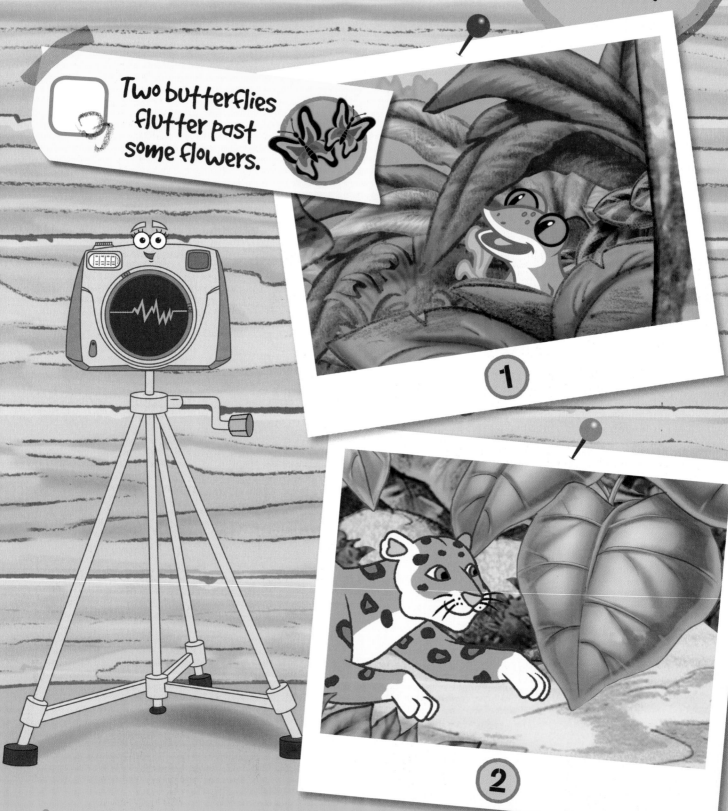

1

2

4 Sammy the sloth has woken up!

1 A frog looks around the rainforest.

3

2 Here comes Mama Jaguar!

4

SPANISH

well done

muy bien

say 'mwee bee-EHN'

We found Mama Jaguar. ¡Muy bien!

Answers on page 68.

29

We need to get across this broken bridge. If I climb on Mama Jaguar's back we can jump across. Jaguars have strong legs that make them really great at jumping. Say "¡Salta!" to help Mama Jaguar jump. We did it!

SPANISH
jump
salta
say 'SAHL-tah'

Baby Jaguar has started climbing up Jaguar Mountain. But he needs to get over those rocks. Jump, Baby Jaguar! Say "¡Salta!" again to help him. He made it!

Uh–oh, now there are some turkey vultures blocking Baby Jaguar's way! We've got to make them move so that Baby Jaguar can climb to the top of the Mountain.

SPANISH
we did it
lo hicimos
say 'loh
ee-SEE-mohs'

Mreow! Mreow!

Turkey vultures are afraid of a jaguar's growl. Let's growl like jaguars to scare them away! Say "Mreow! Mreow!" We scared the turkey vultures away. ¡Lo hicimos!

31

Baby Jaguar needs to climb up the cliff and jump over that rock to reach the top. Say "¡Salta!" one last time. He made it! Jaguars are great climbers and jumpers.

Wow, Baby Jaguar made it all the way to the top of Jaguar Mountain. Mama Jaguar is so proud of him. Thanks for all your help! ¡Gracias!

MISIÓN CUMPLIDA

Can you remember these facts about jaguars?
Draw a circle around each right answer.

Jaguars have really sharp

tails   ears   claws

A jaguar is patterned with

zig-zags   stripes   spots

Jaguars are great at

dancing   climbing   handstands

Answers on page 68.

Jaguar Puzzles

Everyone was so happy to reach the top of Jaguar Mountain! These pictures look the same, but there are five differences between them. Circle the differences in picture 2.

34

Jaguars are great at jumping over things! Put these four things in order from lowest to highest. Write the correct numbers in the boxes, with 1 as the lowest.

Bush **2**

Rock **4**

Log **3**

Puddle **1**

Which of these shadows matches the picture of Baby Jaguar? Draw a circle around the correct one!

① ② ③

Who's Hiding?

Diego and his friends are playing hide-and-seek. Tick (✓) the circle next to each friend as you spot them.

Diego

Sammy

Baby Jaguar

Find six butterflies fluttering about! Which four are the same colour?

Bobo Brothers ⭕

Linda ⭕

Alicia ⭕

Save the Giant Tortoises!

¡Hola! Today at the Rescue Centre there is a giant tortoise called Louie. He's lonely because he's never found another tortoise like him.

We need to find a girl tortoise like Louie, so they can have their own family. Then we can save the giant tortoise species so that they will be around forever!

Let's see if Click can find a girl giant tortoise. Yes, she's found one! This picture is from the Lost Island. That's part of the Galapagos Islands, where Louie is from. Let's go there!

The expedition ship has brought us to the Lost Island, but it can't get to the shore. The rocks are keeping it away. I can hitch a ride on Louie's back – he's great at floating!

We're on the Lost Island. How can we find our way through? Hey, Louie is eating some leaves, and it looks like there's a tunnel behind them! Keep chewing those leaves, Louie – now we can see into the tunnel.

SPANISH
dig
excava
say 'ex-CAH-vah'

Oh no! The other end of the tunnel is blocked, but giant tortoises are great at digging. Come on, Louie, dig! Say "¡Excava!" to help him. Great digging, Louie!

We made it through the tunnel. Click took a photo of Louie when he found the tunnel. Tick (✓) the right photo.

Those booby birds have laid traps made from cactus plants. We need to work out how to get past them. Are you ready? Great, let's go!

Answer on page 69.

Louie has thick skin on his feet, so it doesn't hurt him to step on spiky plants. He has squashed some plants to make a path for us. Find a way through the squashed plants so we can get to Louie!

START

FINISH

How many booby birds can you spot?

You've made Louie so happy! Now let's see what we have learnt about giant tortoises. Draw a circle around each correct answer.

A giant tortoise is good at

floating

sinking

A giant tortoise has thick skin on its

feet

shoes

Giant tortoises are great at

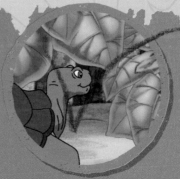

digging

jumping

Answers on page 69.

Louie's Puzzles

Louie is on the beach! There are three other animals here that have a shell, like Louie. Draw a circle around each one.

46

Look at this booby bird. Which of the pictures matches it exactly?

Which of these animals is big and strong enough to take Diego across the water, like Louie did? Tick (✓) the right box.

Spider

Frog

Walrus

Answers on page 69.

Confused Cats!

Those naughty Bobo Brothers have muddled up some wild cat photos! Draw lines to match up the two halves of each photo.

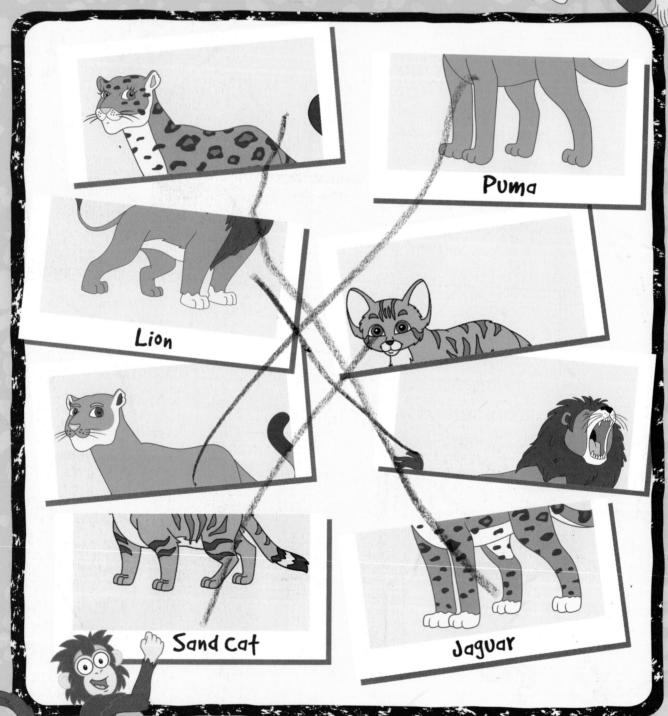

Puma

Lion

Sand Cat

Jaguar

Rainforest Rhapsody

Look at the pictures, then read Diego's story and say the words out loud.

Red-eyed tree frogs

Hummingbirds

Puma

Woodpecker

Howler monkey

Alicia

Tree trunk

Today  is putting on a rainforest concert. The ____ , ____ , ____ and ____ are taking part, but the loud growl of a ____ scares them away! The ____ jump into my pocket, but all the other animals disappear into the rainforest. We need to find them before the concert starts! The ____ use their sticky toes to climb up high so they can see the  .

Next we hear the howling because his foot is trapped. Let's jump as high as we can to rescue the . Well done!

Now we can hear the drumming sound the makes as he taps on a hollow .

We found all the animals and 's concert can begin at last. Thanks!

Jump just like a red-eyed tree frog! Great!

51

Rainforest Puzzles

Put a tick (✓) by the three animals that are good at jumping! Then put a cross (x) by the three animals which aren't.

Elephant

Monkey

Tortoise

Frog

Hippo

Jaguar

There are three pairs of hummingbirds here. Draw lines to match them up, then circle the one that doesn't have a pair.

The woodpecker wants some more wood to tap on! Which line will lead him to the log?

1

2

3

Answers on page 69.

Animal Homes

Do you know where these different animals live? Draw a line from each animal to its home.

Now make a noise like your favourite animal, and act like them too!

Find It!

Those naughty Bobo Brothers have hidden things all around the Animal Rescue Centre. Put a tick (✓) in the circles below when you find each object.

A Blue Morpho Butterfly is Born

¡Hola! Look at the cocoon on this branch. Inside is a blue morpho butterfly. A caterpillar makes a cocoon, and stays inside until it becomes a butterfly!

Hey, the butterfly is coming out! Oh no, Baby Jaguar jumped up and scared him away. We need to find out where he's gone.

Click has found the butterfly in a cold cave. Blue morpho butterflies live in trees – cold places make them sick so they can't fly!

SPANISH
let's go
vámonos
say 'VAH-moh-nohs'

We've got to get him out of the cave and take him back to the warm rainforest. Come on. ¡Vámonos!

There are some other animals that like warm places, like Blue Morpho Butterfly. But some animals like cold places!

Draw lines to match each of these animals to a hot place or a cold place!

Polar bear

Monkey

Penguin   Jaguar   Baby seal   Macaw

Those naughty Bobo Brothers are blocking the cave's entrance with rocks. Shout "Freeze, Bobos!" to stop them. Great, we're in!

I'm going to need Rescue Pack's help to see in this dark cave!

Tick the box next to the thing that Rescue Pack should turn into to help Diego see in the dark!

Great, Rescue Pack turned into a head lamp! Now let's look for the blue morpho butterfly in the cave. Point to him when you spot him. What other animals are here?

We found the blue morpho butterfly! Now let's take him back to the rainforest.

Answers on page 69.

We're almost back in the rainforest, but these jay birds are in our way. Blue Morpho Butterfly can flap his wings to show the different sides – this scares the jay birds away. Flap your arms like a butterfly's wings, too!

Well done! Blue Morpho Butterfly is back in the rainforest, safe and sound. He's even made friends with Baby Jaguar. We did it!

MISIÓN CUMPLIDA

What a rescue – well done! What have you found out about blue morpho butterflies? Read the questions, then draw a circle around each correct picture.

Does a blue morpho butterfly have patterns on its wings or mouth?

wings

mouth

Does a blue morpho butterfly like to be warm or cold?

warm

cold

Does a blue morpho butterfly come out of a cocoon or a box?

cocoon

box

Butterfly Puzzles

Do you remember how a butterfly grows? Finish writing the numbers to put the stages in order.

A caterpillar hatches from an egg!

Butterfly

Caterpillar

Cocoon

Egg

Find the butterfly whose wings don't match each other. Write the answer in the box.

Finish this drawing of a butterfly by drawing in the missing half so the wings match. Colour it in, too!

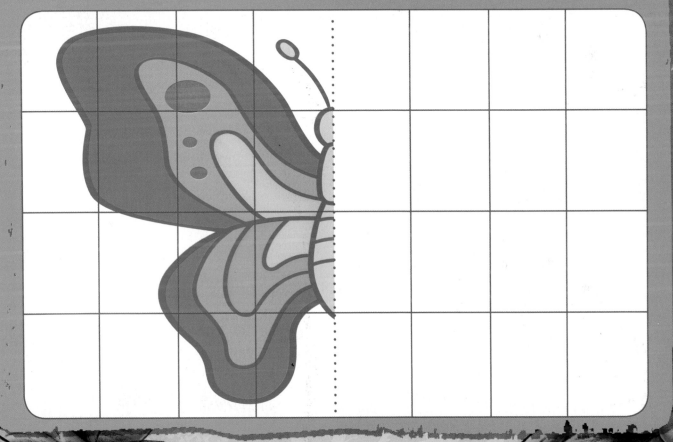

Answer on page 69.

3

4

Answers on page 69.

Answers

p10-11

p13

p15 False, true, true.

p16

p17

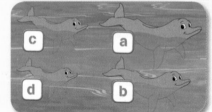

p18-19

p22

p23 The baby gorillas wore a crown.

p28-29

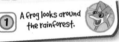

p33 Claws; spots; climbing.

p34

p35

Number 2 is the matching shadow.

p36-37

There are four yellow butterflies.

p41

p42–43

There are seven booby birds.

p45 Floating; feet; digging.

p46 The turtle, crab and snail have shells.

p47 Picture 3 is the matching booby bird.
A walrus could carry Diego.

p48

p49

p52 The monkey, frog and jaguar are
all good at jumping.

p53

Line 3 leads to the wood.

p54

p55

p58–59 The monkey, jaguar and macaw
like hot places. The polar bear,
penguin and baby seal like
cold places.

p61 The butterfly is on a rock at the right.
You can also see an owl and two bats.

p63 Wings; warm; cocoon.

p64 1 – Egg; 2 – Caterpillar;
3 – Cocoon; 4 – Butterfly.

p65 Number 2's wings don't match.

p66–67 1 – Snake; 2 – Tortoise; 3 – Crocodile;
4 – Macaw; 5 – Jaguar; 6 – Ladybird.

The snails are on pages 9, 14, 24, 25, 30,
36, 40, 44, 46 & 60.